To Mark
From Nanny + Scott
Happy Birthday 1975

BASIC BIBLE READER: GRADE ONE

I read about

God's Love

by Carol Ferntheil

Illustrated by

Jane March

STANDARD PUBLISHING
CINCINNATI, OHIO   2711

DEDICATION

This book is lovingly dedicated to those boys and girls who are beginning to read for themselves the wonderful story of God's love.

FOLLOWING A TRADITION

The new Basic Bible Readers are a beautiful, up-to-date edition of the famous Standard Bible Story Readers, by Lillie A. Faris, that were first printed in 1925. More than a million copies have been added to the libraries of homes, schools, and churches in the past four decades.

The best of the former readers has been retained in this new series, including the favorite Bible stories that forever appeal to our children. However, all of the illustrations are completely new—drawn by noted children's artists of today.

Introduction

The original intent of public school education was to make it possible for each person to read the Bible for himself. But the Bible and its stories are rarely used in public schools today. Thus it is necessary for parents and Bible-school teachers to provide Bible training in every possible way.

Before he is ready to read, the child should have Bible stories read to him. You may find this book useful as a family Bible-story book, a book to be read to the preschool child as well as a book to be read by the child who has almost completed the first grade in school. By all means, read the stories directly from the Bible, too, so that the child will understand that the stories come directly from God's Word.

While this reader will probably be most used in the home, it is valuable for the Bible school too. Copies should be in the church library so that teachers and parents may borrow them for reference or for inspection in deciding what to buy. The teacher may place the book on the reading table for use before class or in free Bible activity time. If several copies are available, the teacher may like to have the class read together some of the stories. Or sections may be copied on a reading chart or chalkboard for the class to read together.

It will be necessary for you to teach your beginning reader the new Bible words in this book. Help the child with the pronunciation, using the word lists in the back of this book for review and drill. Associate the word with a picture in this book or in a Bible picture dictionary. Pictures are extremely important in helping the child both to understand what he is reading and to remember it by retaining a visual image in his mind.

I Read About God's Love is the second in a series especially designed as supplementary reading for primary-grade pupils. Of the wealth of Bible stories available, each one is selected for the age for which it has a special appeal. Stories about Jesus are emphasized in each Basic Bible Reader; and in this way, although simplified, the stories help carry out the New Testament purpose of leading the reader to know and love Jesus and to want to follow and obey Him. The stories from the Old Testament, with their emphasis on worship, prayer, honesty, kindness, courage, and forgiveness, are valuable helps for character development while they fulfill their major purpose of bringing the child closer to an understanding of God.

Stories

Bible Verses

Poems

Also in This Book

AWAY
in a
MANGER

Away in a manger,
No crib for a bed,
The little Lord Jesus
Laid down His sweet head.
The stars in the sky
Looked down where He lay,
The little Lord Jesus
Asleep on the hay.

The cattle are lowing,
   The baby awakes,
But little Lord Jesus,
   No crying He makes.
I love Thee, Lord Jesus,
   Look down from the sky,
And stay by my bedside
   Till morning is nigh.

—Martin Luther

9

MARY AND JOSEPH

A man and a woman were on a trip.
The man was Joseph.
The woman was Mary.
They were very tired.
They had come a long way.
When they came to the town of
Bethlehem, they were happy.

"Now we can stop," said Joseph.
"Now we can go to sleep," said Mary.
Joseph knocked on the door of the inn.
The innkeeper said, "No room here."
Mary and Joseph went to another house.
There was no room.
They went to another, and another.
Where could they stay?

They went to another place.
Joseph knocked again.
The man said, "No room here."
Then he thought again.
"You can stay in my stable
with the cows and sheep, if you want to."
So Mary and Joseph went into the
stable.
That night baby Jesus was born.
Mary placed Him in a manger
filled with hay.

It was night in a country far away.
The stars were very bright.
The little children were asleep.
The mothers and fathers were asleep.
In the little town of Bethlehem,
Mary and Joseph were not asleep.
They were in the stable of the inn.

The ANGELS and the SHEPHERDS

They were looking at the baby Jesus.
The baby Jesus was in the manger.
The baby Jesus was God's Son.
Mary loved Him very much.
Out on a hill some shepherds
were watching their sheep.
The shepherds were not asleep.

The shepherds watched their sheep
all the time.

They did not want any of the sheep
to get away.

They did not want anything
to hurt the sheep.

So they watched and watched.

They sat on the ground and talked.

They watched the moon and stars.

Then something great happened.

A bright light shone in the sky.

It was brighter than the stars.

It shone,

      and it shone,

           and it shone.

The shepherds saw the bright light.

They saw an angel in the light.

The angel talked to the shepherds.

They had never heard an angel talk.

The angel said, "I bring you good news.
I have come to tell you that Jesus is born.
You will find Him in the town.
You will find Him in a stable.
You will find Him in a manger."

The shepherds heard every word.

Then more angels came.

Many angels came until the sky
seemed to be full of them.

All the angels sang together.

When the angels went away,
the shepherds said to each other,
"Let us go to Bethlehem
and see what has happened."

They went as fast as they could.

They did just what the angel
told them to do.

They went to the stable.

They found the baby Jesus there.

The shepherds were glad.
They loved the baby Jesus.
They said thank you to God
for sending His Son to be their king.
The shepherds said, "We shall always
love the baby Jesus. The baby Jesus
is God's own Son."

JESUS, FRIEND OF LITTLE CHILDREN

Jesus, friend of little children,
   Be a friend to me;
Take my hand and ever keep me
   Close to Thee.

Teach me how to grow in goodness
   Daily as I grow;
Thou hast been a child,
   And surely Thou dost know.

—*Walter J. Mathams*

17

Once there was a bright star.
It was brighter than the other stars.
It twinkled,
            and it twinkled,
                        and it twinkled.
It made the sky look pretty.
The star wanted to tell a story.
Some Wise-men were watching it.

18

the *Wonderful Star*

They were looking at the sky.
They seemed to be looking
for a new star in the sky.
They looked,
      and they looked,
           and they looked.
At last they saw a very bright star.
It was brighter than all the others.

They said, "Oh, there is a new star.
It must be the bright new star
for which we have been looking.
It must be the bright new star
that tells us about the new King."

The Wise-men were happy and glad
to see the new star.

It seemed to say to them,
"Come with me, and I will show you
where to find the baby Jesus."

The Wise-men began to get ready to go.
They would ride on big camels.
They said, "Let us take some presents
to the new baby King."
One Wise-man had very much gold.
One Wise-man had sweet perfume.
Another Wise-man had presents
for the baby Jesus, too.
They got on the camels' backs.

The Wise-men rode a long, long way.
They watched the bright star.
It shone as brightly as it could.
It shone,

and it shone,

and it shone.
The camels walked on and on.
They went very far.
Some times the Wise-men would get
down from the camels' backs.

The Wise-men went to see King Herod.

They said, "King Herod, can you tell us
where to find the new baby King?
We have seen His star in the East.
We want to worship Him."

King Herod heard from his helpers
that Jesus was to be born in Bethlehem.

He told the Wise-men this and said,
"When you find Him, come back.
I want to see Him, too."

The Wise-men got on their camels.
The star went before them.
It stopped over the house
where the baby Jesus was.

The Wise-men took their presents
into the house to the baby Jesus.

They gave the presents to Jesus.

They were very happy because
they had seen the new baby King.

22

23

Now when Jesus was born
in Bethlehem of Judaea
in the days of Herod the king,
behold, there came wise men
from the east to Jerusalem,
Saying, Where is he
that is born King of the Jews?
for we have seen his star
in the east, and are come
to worship him.

.   .   .

When they had heard the
king, they departed; and, lo, the
star, which they saw in the east,

24

BIBLE SAYS

went before them, till it came
and stood over where
the young child was.

. . .

And when they were come
into the house, they saw
the young child with Mary
his mother, and fell down,
and worshipped him: and
when they had opened their
treasures, they presented
unto him gifts; gold, and
frankincense, and myrrh.

—*Matthew 2:1, 2, 9, 11*

25

How I Wish I Knew

Little stars that twinkle
   In the heavens blue,
I have often wondered
   If you ever knew
How there shone one like you,
   Leading wise old men
From the East, a long way
   Down to Bethlehem.

Did you see the presents
   They in love had brought?
Did you see the home which
   They in wonder sought?
Little stars that twinkle
   In the heavens blue,
All that you knew of Jesus,
   How I wish I knew!

—*Unknown*

GOD IS LOVE

"God is love,"
    The squirrel chatters,
As he gathers
    Winter's food.
"And my heart
    Is full of gladness:
God is great
    And He is good."

"God is love,"
  The little birdies,
In their nest
  Up in the tree,
Seem to say
  In their sweet voices,
"God is love,"
  To you and me.

"God is love,"
 The snowflakes whisper,
As they linger in the air.
"God is love,"
 The breezes murmur,
As they meet us everywhere.

Little stars that
    Shine in heaven,
As they twinkle far above,
Peeping, smiling at each other,
Whisper gently,
    "God is love."

After the storm the rainbow,
　　Bending far above,
Seems to say,
　　In her own sweet way,
"Children, God is love."

"God is love."
I'm sure He watches
O'er the squirrels
And birdies, too.
I'm sure He is looking,
Lovingly, at me and you.

—*Unknown*

IN THE TEMPLE

Once there was a good old man.
His name was Simeon.

Simeon loved God's house.
It was called the temple.

He was glad when he went
to the temple.

Simeon had always tried to do
just what God wanted him to do.

Many times Simeon talked to God.

Many times God talked to Simeon.

One day God said, "Simeon,
some day you shall see Jesus."

Simeon was very glad, for he knew
that Jesus was to be the new King.

He kept looking for the new King.

Mary and Joseph lived far away
from the temple.

They wanted to take the baby Jesus
to God's house.

They had a long, long trip.

Outside the temple they saw a man
who had doves to sell.

People would buy the doves and
give them to God.

Mary and Joseph wanted to do
what God told them to do.

"We shall buy two doves," said Joseph.
"We want to do as God told us to do."

Joseph took the doves into the temple.

Mary took Jesus into the temple.

The old man Simeon came to Mary
and took baby Jesus in his arms.

Then God told Simeon that
the baby was Jesus.

Simeon was very happy.

One day God had said, "Simeon,
some day you shall see Jesus."

Now Simeon looked at the baby Jesus.

He held the baby in his arms.

He said many beautiful things
about the baby Jesus.

Jesus was the new King.

A good woman lived in the temple.
Her name was Anna.
Anna knew that Jesus was coming.
She was looking for Him, too.
Anna saw Simeon holding the baby.
She came to look at Him.
She was glad to see the baby Jesus.
Anna knew He was the new King.
She told many people about Jesus.
She said He was the new King.

Mary and Joseph said thank you to God.
They said, "Thank you for baby Jesus."
They gave the two doves to God.
They were glad to come to God's house
and to bring the baby Jesus.
They were glad to hear Simeon and
Anna say good things about baby Jesus.
Then Mary and Joseph
took Jesus home again.

A
LONG
TRIP

The shepherds were glad
when the baby Jesus was born.
They went to see Him.
The Wise-men were glad, too.
They took beautiful presents to Jesus.
There was an old king named Herod.
He was not glad.
He did not like the baby Jesus.
Herod said, "I am the king.
I do not want Jesus to be king."

King Herod talked to the Wise-men.

He said, "Come and tell me
when you find the baby Jesus.
I want to worship Him, too."

Herod was a bad king.
He did not really want
to worship the baby Jesus.

Herod wanted to hurt the baby.
God would not let this happen.
God said to the Wise-men,
"Do not go back to see the king.
Go home another way."
The Wise-men did not go back.
They went home another way.

An angel came to Joseph.
The angel said to Joseph,
"The bad king wants to hurt Jesus.
Take Mary and Jesus away.
Take them on a long trip."
Joseph took Mary and Jesus away.
They went on a long, long trip.
Mary and Jesus rode on a little donkey.
Joseph walked beside them.
They went far away from the king.

After that the bad king died.
The angel came to Joseph again.
The angel said to Joseph,
"Take Mary and Jesus home again.
Jesus will be safe now."
Joseph and Mary were very happy.
They were glad to go home again.
Mary and Jesus rode the little donkey.
They took the long trip home again.

OUR DAILY
BREAD

A little boy's mother gave him
a brown roll for his breakfast.

The little boy said, "Thank you, Mother.
Thank you for my good brown roll."

The mother said,
"Don't thank me; thank Mr. Baker."
The little boy ran to Mr. Baker.
He said, "Thank you, Mr. Baker.
Thank you for my good brown roll."
Mr. Baker said,
"Don't thank me; thank Mr. Farmer."

The little boy ran to Mr. Farmer.

He said, "Thank you, Mr. Farmer.

Thank you for my good brown roll."

Mr. Farmer said,

"Don't thank me; thank Mr. Rain.

I only planted the wheat."

The boy saw the clouds in the sky.

He saw the rain falling.

He said, "Thank you, Mr. Rain.
Thank you for my good brown roll."

Mr. Rain said,
"Don't thank me; thank Mr. Sun.
I only helped a little."

Mr. Sun began to shine.

The boy said, "Thank you, Mr. Sun.
Thank you for my good brown roll."
The sun said, "Don't thank me.
Thank God who made me."
The little boy sat down at the table.
He said, "Thank you, God.
Thank you for my good brown roll."

Beautiful Things

Each little flower that opens,
    Each little bird that sings,
God made their glowing colors;
    He made their tiny wings.

Yes, all things bright and beautiful,
    All creatures great and small,
All things wise and wonderful,
    The Lord God made them all.

—Cecil Alexander

JESUS in the TEMPLE

Jesus grew to be a big, strong boy.
One day Mary said,
"Jesus is a big boy and a good helper.
Let us take Him with us to God's house."
Joseph said, "Yes,
Jesus is twelve years old.
We shall take Him to the temple."
They went a long way to Jerusalem.
Jesus saw God's beautiful house.
They prayed to God there.

Then it was time to go home.
Joseph and Mary had many friends.
They thought Jesus was with friends.
They went a long way.

Mary began to look for Jesus.
Joseph asked their friends,
"Have you seen Jesus?"
Their friends had not seen Him.
Mary said, "We must go back
to Jerusalem. We must find Jesus."
They looked for three long days.

At last they went to God's house.
There they found Jesus.
He was talking with some teachers.
Mary said, "Son, why did you do this?
We looked and looked for you."
Jesus said, "Do you not know
I must do my Father's work?"
Then He went home with Mary and
Joseph.
He did just what they told Him.
He wanted to grow bigger and stronger.
Then He could do God's work.

THE SHEPHERD PSALM

The Lord is my shepherd;
I shall not want.

He maketh me to lie down
in green pastures:

He leadeth me beside the
still waters.

—Psalm 23.

A LITTLE SICK BOY

Once there was a great man.
He lived in a big city.
He had a good little boy.
He loved his little boy very much.
One day the little boy was sick.
He was very hot.
He could not eat.
He was very sick.

The father said, "We must find Jesus.
He can help my little boy."
They knew that Jesus
was not too far away.
The father said, "I shall go after Him.
I know He will come.
I know He will help my little boy."
He went as fast as he could.

At last he found Jesus.
He fell down at Jesus' feet.
He said, "Oh, Jesus,
will you come to my house?
My little boy is very sick.
I know you can make him well."
Jesus was kind to the man.
But the man was so afraid
that the little boy would die.
"Please come," he asked Jesus.
"Please make my little boy well."

Jesus knew that it would take
a long time to go to see the boy.

He knew how sad the man was.

He knew how hard it would be
for the man to wait till he got home.

So the good, kind Jesus thought,
I shall not make him wait.

I shall make the little boy well.

Jesus looked at the man and said,
"Go home, your son is well."

The man was so glad!

He knew what Jesus said was true.

He knew that Jesus could help
his little boy.

He was very happy.

He started home right away.

It took a long time to go back
to his own city.

He saw some men run to meet him.

They were calling to him.

They said, "Your little boy is better.
He is well again."

The man said, "When did he get better?"

The men told him which day
the boy was better.

The man said, "Oh, that was the time
when I talked to Jesus."

The man ran home.

The little boy was well.

The man told his family about the good, kind Jesus.

They all said thank you to Jesus for helping the little boy.

MY BEAUTIFUL PALACE

A beautiful palace
    My King gave to me,
And all through my lifetime
    My home it will be.
I call it my body,
    To use as I will,
But this I remember,
    That God owns it still.

From things that would harm it,
    I'll keep it away,
And carefully guard it
    By night and by day.
Its windows and doors
    Are my lips, ears, and eyes.
Dear King, help me use them
    In ways that are wise.

—Louise M. Oglevee

THAT SWEET STORY of OLD

I think when I read
That sweet story of old,
When Jesus was here among men,
How He called little children
As lambs to His fold,
I should like to have been with Him then.

I wish that His hands
Had been placed on my head;
That His arms had been thrown around me,
And that I might have seen
His kind look when He said,
"Let the little ones come unto me."

—*Jemima Luke*

Morning Prayer

Father, we thank Thee for the night
And for the pleasant morning light,
For rest and food and loving care,
And all that makes the day so fair.

Help us to do
the things we should,
To be to others
kind and good.
In all we do,
in work or play,
To grow more
loving every day.

—*Rebecca J. Weston*

Evening Prayer

Jesus, tender Shepherd, hear me;
Bless Thy little lamb tonight:
Through the darkness be Thou near me,
Keep me safe till morning light.

All this day
Thy hand has led me,
    And I thank Thee
for Thy care;
    Thou hast warmed
me, clothed me, fed me;
    Listen to my
evening prayer.

—*M. Duncan*

JESUS LOVES THE LITTLE CHILDREN

Jesus grew to be a man.
He loved all the people.
He helped many sick people.

One day Jesus was very busy.

Many people wanted to see Him.

Many sick people came to Jesus
for help.

Jesus was making them well.

Some mothers were watching.

One mother said to the others,
"If Jesus would touch our children,
they would be very happy."

Then another mother said,
"If He would just put His hands
on their heads, I should be glad."
The mothers thought they would see
if they could talk with Jesus.
They took their little children
and tried to get near Jesus.
Some of Jesus' helpers thought
that it would not be right
for Jesus to talk to the children.
They said, "Don't bring the children.
Jesus has no time for them."

Jesus saw what His helpers were doing.
He said, "Let the little children come."
They came very near to Him.
He took them in His arms.
He put His hands on their heads.
He loved the children very much.
The children loved Jesus, too.

Jesus showed that He was happy
to see the children. He said,
"Suffer the little children
to come unto me,
and forbid them not,
for of such is the kingdom of heaven."

Jesus' helpers saw that
He loved the children.

Then Jesus talked to them. He said,
"You must become like these children
if you want to be great
in the kingdom of heaven."

Kind Words

Kind hearts are the gardens,
    Kind thoughts are the roots,
Kind words are the flowers,
    Kind deeds are the fruits.

Take care of the gardens,
    And keep them from weeds.
Fill, fill them with flowers,
    Kind words and kind deeds.

—*Longfellow*

Happy Days

Two eyes to see nice things to do;
Two lips to smile the whole day through;
Two ears to hear what others say;
Two hands to put the toys away;
A tongue to speak kind words each day;
A loving heart to work and play;
Two feet that errands gladly run—
Make happy days for everyone.

—*Louise M. Oglevee*

A LITTLE SICK GIRL

A happy family lived in the land where Jesus was.

There was a mother and a father and a little girl.

They lived in a beautiful home.

They loved each other very much.

The father had much money.
He was a very good man, too.
The little girl was good and kind.
She had many friends.

One day the little girl was very sick.
"I feel so hot," she said.
"I don't want anything to eat."
She could not get out of bed.
Her mother and father said,
"We must help our little girl.
We must do everything to make her well."
They tried and tried to help her.
But she was still sick.

One day the father said,
"I know one more thing to do.
I shall go for Jesus.
He has helped many sick people
to get well again.

He will make our little girl well.
I know He will come.
I shall go and ask Him."

The father ran to find Jesus.
There were many people around Jesus.
Jesus was helping the sick people.
He was making them well.
The father ran to Jesus and said,
"Our little girl is very sick.
Come and put your hands on her.

I know that you can
make her well."

Then a man ran
to see the father.
He said, "It is too late.
Your little girl
is dead."

Jesus looked at the sad father.
He said, "Do not be afraid."
Jesus went home with the man.
Many people were there.
Jesus said, "Why are you crying?
The little girl is not dead.
She is just asleep."

Then the mother and father took Jesus
to the room where the little girl was.

Jesus went over to the bed.

He took her hand and said,
"Little girl, stand up."

A great thing happened!
The little girl stood up.
Jesus said, "Give her some food."
The mother and father were happy.
All the people were happy.
They said, "Thank you, Jesus.
Thank you for helping our little girl.
Thank you for making her well."

Little Lambs

Little lambs, so white and fair,
Are the loving shepherd's care;
Now he leads their tender feet
Into pastures green and sweet.

Now they listen and obey,
Going where he leads the way;
Heavenly Father, may we be
Thus obedient unto Thee.

—Unknown

LITTLE CHILDREN LOVE JESUS

Jesus was riding along the road.
He was riding a little donkey.
The children were happy to see Him.
"Here comes Jesus," they called.

Many of His friends were with Him.
They knew that Jesus was going away.
He told them that He was going
to live with His Father in heaven.

"We shall tell Him how we love Him,"
the people said.

"Jesus has made us happy."

The children were calling and singing.

All the people began to sing,
"Hosanna in the highest."

They were very happy.

They wanted to make the way beautiful
for Jesus to come along.

They put leaves in the street.

They put flowers all around.

Some people put their coats
in the street.

They waved branches and flowers.

They showed Jesus that
they loved Him.

Children always love to sing
to Jesus. This is what we sing today:
    "Praise Him, praise Him,
    All ye little children.
      God is love!
      God is love."

A Little Lost Lamb

There was a kind shepherd man.
He had 100 sheep.
Some of the sheep were big.
Some of the sheep were little.
The shepherd loved his sheep.
He gave each one a name.
One little lamb was Snowball.
Snowball was white and clean.
The shepherd took good care
of his sheep.
He looked for green grass.
He looked for cold water.
He watched the sheep every day.

One day Snowball went too far away.
He could not find the shepherd.
He was lost!

The shepherd did not miss him at first.
He took all the sheep home.
He counted the sheep as he put them
into the fold for the night.
He counted 99 sheep.
One lamb was lost!
The shepherd called all the sheep.
He called, "Snowball! Snowball!"
But Snowball did not come.
Snowball was lost!

The shepherd went to look for him.
He looked and looked.
At last he heard a lamb crying.
The lamb said, "Baa! Baa!"
The shepherd found Snowball.
He picked up the lamb in his arms.
He took him home.
The shepherd was happy because
he had found his little lost lamb.

JESUS' LITTLE LAMB

I am Jesus' little lamb,
Happy all day long I am.
He will keep me safe, I know,
    For I'm His lamb.

By His staff I'm led along,
Guarded by His arm so strong,
I'm so happy all day long,
    For I'm His lamb.

—Unknown

NOAH

There were many people on earth.
God in heaven looked on them.
He saw that the people did not
try to be good.

God was not happy with the people.
He looked and looked for a good man.
And He saw Noah.
Noah was a good man
who would work for God.

God said, "Noah, you are a good man.
I want you to do just what
I tell you to do.
If you will do as I say,
you will be safe."

Then God told Noah that
it would rain and rain.

The water in the rivers would get
higher and higher.

It would get higher than the trees.

God told Noah to build a boat
called an ark.

God said, "Make the ark
as high as I say.
Make the ark this wide.
Make the ark this long.
Make one big door.
Make one big window."

Noah and his sons did build the ark.
They did just what God said.

Then God said, "Take your family.
Take lots of food.
Go into the ark.
You will be there a long time."
Noah and his wife went into the ark.
All of his family went into the ark.
They did just what God said.

Noah took all the animals
into the ark.

How many different animals and birds
do you know?

Noah took all of them into the ark.
Two by two, the animals walked in.
Two by two, the birds flew in.

God shut the door of the ark.
It began to rain.

It rained,

and it rained,

and it rained!

It rained for many days and nights.
Water was over everything.
But the big ark was on the water.
Noah and his family were not afraid.
God was taking care of them.
Then one day the rain stopped.
The water began to go down.
Noah sent out a dove.

When the dove did not come back,
Noah knew that the water was gone.

When the water went away,
the ark was on a mountain.

Noah and his family walked outside.
"Thank you, God," they said at once.
God was happy to hear them pray.

God said, "I will never send
so much water again.
The rainbow will tell you this
when you see it in the sky."

Then Noah saw a beautiful rainbow—
red, orange, yellow, green, blue, violet.

Noah said, "God has been good to us.
The rainbow will tell us that
God will always keep His word."

GOD'S RAINBOW

"While the earth remaineth,
seedtime and harvest,
and cold and heat,
and summer and winter,
and day and night shall not cease.

"I do set my bow in the cloud,
and it shall be for a token
of a covenant between me and the earth. . .
and the waters shall no more
become a flood to destroy all flesh."

—*Genesis 8:22; 9:13, 15*

90

My Father's Care

How strong and sweet my Father's care,
That, round about me like the air,
Is with me always, everywhere,
Is with me always, everywhere!
    He cares for me.

Oh, keep me ever in Thy love,
Dear Father, watching from above,
And let me still Thy mercy prove,
And let me still Thy mercy prove,
    And care for me.

—Unknown

Father, Lead Me Day by Day

Father, lead me day by day,
Ever in Thine own good way;
Teach me to be pure and true;
Show me what I ought to do.

—Unknown

JOSEPH

Joseph was a little boy.
He had many big brothers.
He had a kind father named Jacob.
Jacob had many things.
He had cows and sheep and camels.
His sons took care of the animals.

Joseph said, "I shall be a helper, too.
I shall watch the sheep."
But his big brothers said,
"What can you do to help?
You are just a little boy.
You should stay at home."
They were not kind to Joseph.

Jacob loved his little son.
He wanted to make him happy.
He gave Joseph a beautiful coat.
It had many pretty colors in it.
Joseph put on his beautiful coat.
He was very happy.
He said, "Thank you, Father."
Jacob was happy and pleased, too.
Jacob said, "Now I want you to help me.
I want to hear from your brothers.
They are far away with the sheep.
Go and find them."

Joseph put on his beautiful coat.
He walked and walked.
He asked many people,
"Did you see my brothers?"

At last Joseph found his brothers.

They were still not kind.

They said, "Let us do something
with this boy and his coat.
He must not go home."

They saw some people from far away
coming along the road.

They called, "Would you like
to buy a boy? Would you like a helper?"

The people took Joseph with them.

The brothers took his beautiful coat.

They took it home to Jacob.

They said, "Joseph is gone.
See! Here is his coat."

Jacob was very sad.

He thought Joseph was dead.

But Joseph was in a land far away.

The king liked him very much.

The king made him a ruler, too.

After many years, Joseph saw
his brothers.

He was kind to them.

He asked them to bring his father.

Jacob was happy to see his son.

He was happy to see that
Joseph was a ruler like the king.

The brothers wished they had been kind.

They wanted to be friends with Joseph.

Joseph was good to all of them.

Thank You, God

Thank you for the world so sweet,
Thank you for the food we eat,
Thank you for the birds that sing,
Thank you, God, for everything.

—*Unknown*

A Little
Basket Boat

Once there was an old king.

He was not kind to the people.

He was always thinking of
bad things to do.

One day he said to his soldiers,
"I do not like these people.

I want you to kill all the boy babies.

I do not want to see them any more."

One mother knew what the bad king
was going to do.

She had a sweet little baby boy.

She wanted to keep him safe.

He had a sister named Miriam.

She wanted to help, too.

The mother said, "Oh, the king
must not hurt my little baby boy.
I must think of a plan.
What shall I do?"

She thought of a good plan.
She found lots of long grass.
She made it into a basket.
The basket was like a little boat.

Miriam wanted to help her mother.

She said, "I shall get more grass. I shall find a soft blanket to put inside the basket."

When the basket was ready, it was a soft little baby bed.

The mother gave her baby a hug and put him in the basket.

Miriam gave the baby a hug, too.

She said, "Be good, little brother. I shall take care of you."

Miriam and her mother took the little basket away from home.

They went to the river.

The mother said, "Let us hide the basket in the tall grass."

They put the basket in the water. It was like a little boat.

The baby was safe and warm.

Miriam said, "I shall hide behind
the tall grass. I shall watch the baby."

She waited to see
what would happen.

Maybe someone would find the baby
and be good to him.

Their mother went home again.

Miriam watched the basket boat.
Soon the princess came along.
She saw the little basket boat.
She said to her friends,
"Bring me that little basket."
Her friends went into the water.
They gave her the basket.

She looked in the basket.
She found the baby boy!
The baby was crying.
The princess held him in her arms.
He stopped crying and looked at her.
She said, "He is a beautiful baby.
I think I shall keep him.
He can live with me and be my son.
I shall name him Moses,
because I took him out of the water."
Now Miriam knew the baby was safe.
She ran to talk to the princess.

She said, "Do you want someone
to care for the baby?"

The princess said, "Yes, I do.
Can you find someone for me?"

Miriam ran home to get her mother.
Her mother was going to care for the baby.

Baby Moses was safe and well.

Samuel

Hannah was very sad.
She did not have a girl or boy.
She went to the temple to pray.
Hannah prayed to God,
"Please send me a baby boy.
If I have a baby boy,
I will take him to the temple
to be a helper."
God heard Hannah's prayer.
He gave her a baby boy named Samuel.
She took good care of the boy.
She told him about God's house.
When Samuel grew big enough,
Hannah took him to God's house.
She said, "Now Samuel is big enough
to be a helper in God's house.
He is going to work for God."

Samuel lived in the temple.
Some times Hannah came to see him.
Every year she made him a new coat.

Each time Samuel said, "Thank you.
Thank you for my pretty new coat.
I will try to be a good helper."

Eli was an old man. He had worked
in God's house a long time.

Eli showed Samuel what to do.

One night Eli had gone to bed.

Samuel was in bed in his room.

The voice of God called, "Samuel!"

Samuel ran to Eli's room.
He said, "Here I am."

Eli said, "I did not call you."

Samuel went back to bed.

Again the voice of God called, "Samuel!"

Samuel ran to Eli's room.

Eli said, "I did not call you."

Samuel went back to bed.

He heard the voice again.

Eli said, "God must be calling you."

The next time the voice called,
Samuel answered, "Talk to me, Lord,
for I hear you."

Then God talked to Samuel.

Samuel told Eli what God said.
Then Eli knew that God had called
Samuel. God had talked to him.
Samuel was going to be one of
God's good helpers.

THE FATHER'S PLAN

Each little creature our Father
    has made
Has a home that is planned just
    for him—
A nest for the birds
and a hive for the bee,
A burrow for rabbits,
My own house for me
Are a part of our Father's
    great plan.

108

Each little creature our Father
   has made
Thinks his own home the best
   that can be.
The bee loves his hive
And the bird loves his nest;
The rabbit is sure that his burrow
   is best;
And I know that my home is
   best for me.

—*Elizabeth Shields.*

109

A Shepherd Boy

David was a good shepherd.
He took good care of his sheep.
He was very kind to the little lambs.
He loved the sheep and the lambs.
In the morning, David would take
the sheep out in the fields.
He knew the sheep liked to go
where the grass was green.
He looked for a place where
the water was cold.
Some times David would sing.
Some times he would play his harp.
David would play and sing these words:
"God is my shepherd. He helps me
take care of the sheep."
David would sing, "Thank you, God.
Thank you for taking care of me."

One day an old bear ran after
the sheep. It took a lamb.

David was not afraid.

He ran after the bear.

He took the lamb away from the bear.

He hit the bear and killed it.

David said, "God helped me kill the
bear. The little lamb is safe."

112

One day a big lion quietly came up and took a little lamb.

David ran after the lion.

He took the lamb away from the lion.

David killed the lion, too.

David said, "God helped me kill the lion. The little lamb is safe. God takes care of me, too."

LITTLE  BIRDIE

What does little birdie say,
In her nest at peep of day?
"Let me fly," says little birdie—
  "Mother, let me fly away."
    "Birdie, stay a little longer,
    Till the little wings are stronger."
  So she stays a little longer,
    Then she flies away.

What does little baby say,
In her bed at peep of day?
Baby says, like little birdie,
  "Let me rise and fly away."
    "Baby, sleep a little longer,
    Till the little limbs are stronger.
  If she sleeps a little longer,
    Baby, too, shall fly away."

—*Alfred Lord Tennyson*

God's Love

He prayeth best, who loveth best

    All things, both great and small.

For the dear God, who loveth us,

    He made and loveth all.

—*Samuel Coleridge*

A DEN OF LIONS

Once there was a little boy.
His name was Daniel.
Daniel was a very happy boy.
Daniel had a kind mother.
He had a good father.
They told Daniel how to love God.
They told him to do what was right.
They told him how to pray to God.

One time soldiers came to
Daniel's land.

They took many people far away.
Daniel was taken far from home.
He was a very sad boy.

He always did what
his mother and father had told him.

Daniel prayed to God every day.
He asked God to help him.
He tried not to be afraid.

The king saw that Daniel
was a good boy.

He liked to talk to Daniel.
He loved Daniel very much.

When Daniel grew to be a man,
the king gave him things to do.

The king knew that Daniel would
do what was right.

Some of the king's men did not
like Daniel.

They wanted the king to give them
things to do.

They did not want the king
to love Daniel.

These men said, "Oh, king,
we need a new law. Make a law
that people must pray only to you.
If anyone prays another way,
he will be put into a den of lions."

The king did what the men said.

He made the new law.

He did not know that this would hurt
Daniel.

He told all the people that
they must pray only to him.

But Daniel would not pray
to the king. He prayed to God.

118

Daniel prayed to God every morning.
He prayed at lunch time.
He prayed at night.
The king's men began to watch Daniel.
They saw him praying by his window.
They knew he was praying to God.
They saw that he prayed every day.
They wanted to tell the king.
Daniel was not keeping the new law.
He would be put into a den of lions.

There were big lions in the den.
They opened their big mouths.
They made a loud noise.

The men said to the king,
"Oh, king, Daniel is not keeping
your law. He is praying to God."
The king did not know that Daniel was
praying to God every day.
He was very sad.
He did not want to eat any food.
He could not sleep.
He did not want to hear music.

The soldiers came to get Daniel.
They put him in the lions' den.
Something great happened!
God sent an angel to take care of
Daniel. The lions did not make a noise.
They did not open their mouths.

In the morning the king went
to the lions' den.

He called, "Oh, Daniel, is your God
taking care of you?"

Daniel said, "Oh, king, God sent His
angel to shut the lions' mouths.
They have not hurt me. I am safe."

The king was very happy.

He prayed to Daniel's God, too.

A CHILD'S THANKSGIVING

I thank Thee, Father, for Thy love,
    For my dear home so warm and bright;
I thank Thee for the sunny day,
    And for the sleepy, starry night.
I thank Thee for my father's arms,
    So big and strong to hold me near;
I thank Thee for my mother's face;
    I thank Thee for my playmates dear.

I thank Thee for the little birds
    That eat my crumbs upon the sill;
I thank Thee for the pretty snow
    That's coming down so soft and still.
O Father, who made everything,
    Hear me now and every day,
And please read in my little heart
    The thank yous I forgot to say.

New Basic Bible Vocabulary

Basic Bible Reader, Grade One: *I Read About God's Love,* follows the Basic Bible Primer, *I Learn to Read About Jesus.*

I Read About God's Love contains 543 different words. Of this number, 440 are words used in public school pre-primers, primers, and first readers; 17 are the Bible words repeated from *I Learn to Read About Jesus*; and 86 are new Bible words, that is, words in Scripture quotations and words necessary to the Bible stories. The words used in poetry are exempt from the vocabulary control.

The 86 words in the list to follow are the Bible words used first in this book and are a part of the Basic Bible Vocabulary. The words are listed as they first appear in this book.

8. *Poem*
9. *Poem*
10. . . .
11. inn
    innkeeper
    stable
    born
12. . . .
13. Son
14. shone
15. . . .
16. God
17. *Poem*
18. . . .
19. . . .
20. camels
    Wise-man
    perfume
    camels'
21. . . .

22. East
    worship
23. . . .
24. Judaea
    behold
    wise
    Jews
    departed
    lo
25. young
    child
    worshipped
    treasures
    presented
    unto
    gifts
    frankincense
    myrrh
    Matthew
26. . . .

124

27. *Poem*
28. *Poem*
29. *Poem*
30. *Poem*
31. *Poem*
32. *Poem*
33. *Poem*
34. Simeon
35. doves
36. . . .
37. . . .
38. Anna
39. . . .
40. . . .
41. . . .
42. died
43. . . .
44. . . .
45. . . .
46. . . .
47. . . .
48. *Poem*
49. prayed
50. . . .
51. . . .
52. Lord
    maketh
    lie
    pastures
    leadeth
    Psalm
53. . . .
54. sick
55. Jesus'

    die
56. . . .
57. . . .
58. . . .
59. *Poem*
60. *Poem*
61. . . .
62. *Poem*
63. *Poem*
64. . . .
65. . . .
66. . . .
67. suffer
    forbid
    such
    kingdom
    heaven
68. *Poem*
69. *Poem*
70. . . .
71. . . .
72. . . .
73. dead
74. . . .
75. *Poem*
76. . . .
77. . . .
78. Hosanna
    highest
79. . . .
80. . . .
81. baa
82. *Poem*
83. . . .

84. Noah
85. ark
86. . . .
87. . . .
88. pray
89. . . .
90. remaineth
    seedtime
    harvest
    heat
    cease
    bow
    token
    covenant
    between
    flood
    destroy
    flesh
    Genesis
91. *Poem*
92. Jacob
93. . . .
94. . . .
95. ruler
96. . . .
97. *Poem*
98. Miriam
99. . . .
100. . . .

101. . . .
102. princess
    Moses
103. . . .
104. Hannah
    Hannah's
    prayer
    Samuel
105. . . .
106. Eli
    Eli's
107. . . .
108. *Poem*
109. *Poem*
110. . . .
111. David
    harp
112. . . .
113. . . .
114. *Poem*
115. *Poem*
116. Daniel
117. Daniel's
118. law
    den
119. praying
120. . . .
121. . . .
122. *Poem*

Cumulative Basic Bible Vocabulary

Through Grade One

The following list includes all of the words introduced as new Bible words in the Basic Bible Primer and in the Basic Bible Reader, Grade One.

angel
Anna
ark

baa
behold
Bethlehem
between
Bible
born
bow

camel
camels'
cease
child
covenant

Daniel
Daniel's
David
dead
den
departed
destroy
die

died
dove

east
Eli
Eli's

flesh
flood
forbid
frankincense

Genesis
gift
God
God's

Hannah
Hannah's
harp
harvest
heat
heaven
Herod
highest
hosanna

inn
innkeeper

Jacob
Jerusalem
Jesus
Jesus'
Jew
Joseph
Judaea

king
kingdom

law
leadeth
lie
lo
Lord

maketh
manger
Mary
Matthew
Miriam
Moses
myrrh

Noah

pasture
perfume
pray
prayed
prayer

praying
presented
princess
Psalm

remaineth
ruler

Samuel
seedtime
sheep
shepherd
shone
sick
Simeon
son
stable
star
such
suffer

teacher
temple
token
treasure

unto

wise
Wise-man
Wise-men
worship
worshipped

young

128

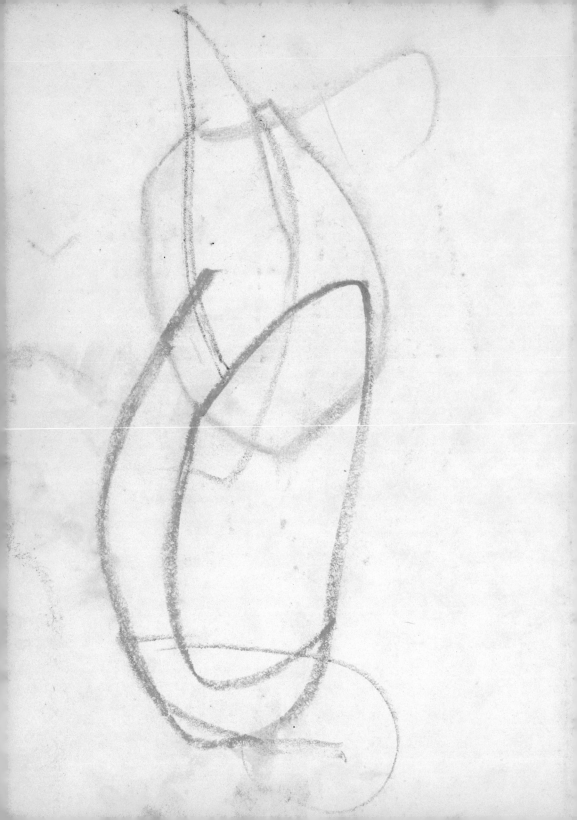